Traditional Black Music

RAGTIME SONG AND DANCE

CHELSEA HOUSE PUBLISHERS

New York   Philadelphia

On the cover Eubie Blake, at the piano, performing Wita Noble Sissle in 1922.

Chelsea House Publishers
Editorial Director   Richard Rennert
Executive Managing Editor   Karyn Gullen Browne
Copy Chief   Robin James
Picture Editor   Adrian G. Allen
Art Director   Robert Mitchell
Manufacturing Director   Gerald Levine
Assistant Art Director   Joan Ferrigno

Staff for Ragtime Song and Dance
Picture Researcher   Villette Harris
Book Layout   John Infantino, Lydia Rivera

First Printing
1   3   5   7   9   8   6   4   2

Library of Congress Cataloging-in-Publication Data
Ragtime song and dance / [compiled by] Jerry Silverman.
1 score. — (Traditional Black music)
For voice and piano: includes chord symbols.
Includes index.
  ISBN 0-7910-1836-9   0-7910-1852-0 (pbk.)
1. Ragtime music—Juvenile. [1. Ragtime music. 2. Jazz. 3. Songs.
4. Afro-Americans—Music.] I. Silverman, Jerry. II. Series.
M1630.18.R187 1994   94-3544
796.42'092—dc20   CIP
                                                      AC M

PICTURE CREDITS
The Bettmann Archive: p. 17; Frank Driggs Collection: pp: 28, 35;
The New York Public Library, Lincoln Center Library for the Per-
forming Arts: p. 5; The New York Public Library at Lincoln Center,
Performing Arts Research Center, New York, cover; Ohio Historical
Society: p. 39; Collection of Duncan P. Scheidt: pp. 11, 45, 52, The
Schomburg Center for Research in Black Culture/The New York
Public Library/Astor, Lenox and Tilden Foundations: pp. 22, 63.

CONTENTS

Author's Preface

The syncopated rhythms and catchy tunes that took the United States and Europe by storm in the last decade of the 19th century and the first decade of the 20th century did not spring fully grown from the fingers of those legendary striped-shirt pianists of barroom and sporting house fame. The music had its roots in the lively Creole dances of antebellum days, filtered through the outrageous minstrel shows and music hall extravaganzas that entertained audiences in the decades after the Civil War. Born without a name, the music was soon to be baptized "rag-time."

Somewhere along the way, rag-time lost its hyphenated spelling and gained a panoply of composer-performers who rivaled in popularity any of the show business stars of later generations. Remarkably, the music achieved almost all of its fame by means of sheet music performed on the parlor piano at home. When they were able, professional ragtime musicians played their songs in music halls and cabarets, but there was no television, or any commercial radio, to readily gain the listeners' attention. In the earliest days of ragtime, in fact, recordings were not yet available to the public.

Ironically, it was white composer John Philip Sousa who first introduced ragtime to a broad audience of Americans—at the 1904 World's Fair in St. Louis, Missouri, where his band thrilled the mostly white crowds with symphonic arrangements of cakewalks and rags. By the time Sousa had played the music for the captivated audiences at the fair, however, black musical giants such as Benjamin R. Harney, Will Marion Cook, and Scott Joplin had been laying the groundwork for ragtime's success—writing the music and performing it live for almost 10 years.

The initial musical impulse of ragtime—its syncopated rhythm—is instrumental in nature. But ragtime lyrics and the flamboyant entertainers who sang them were also an important part of this musical craze. The subject matter of the typical ragtime song varied from the downright hilarious to the merely cute, from the somewhat dated "camp meeting, cakewalk, swell-affair" to the stereotype of the black-face minstrel.

This collection has tried as much as possible to avoid such stereotypes. The compositions included here are either by black masters of the genre or white composers whose works can stand comparison to "the real thing." In addition, the book begins with half a dozen traditional songs that, by virtue of their syncopated melodies, can rightly be regarded as the roots of ragtime.

Jerry Silverman

The Contribution of Blacks to American Art and Culture

Kenneth B. Clark

Historical and contemporary social inequalities have obscured the major contribution of American blacks to American culture. The historical reality of slavery and the combined racial isolation, segregation, and sustained educational inferiority have had deleterious effects. As related pervasive social problems determine and influence the art that any group can not only experience, but also, ironically, the extent to which they can eventually contribute to the society as a whole, this tenet is even more visible when assessing the contributions made by African Americans.

All aspects of the arts have been pursued by black Americans, but music provides a special insight into the persistent and inescapable social forces to which black Americans have been subjected. One can speculate that in their preslavery patterns of life in Africa, blacks used rhythm, melody, and lyrics to hold on to reality, hope, and the acceptance of life. Later, in America, music helped blacks endure the cruelties of slavery. Spirituals and gospel music provided a medium for both communion and communication. As the black experience in America became more complex, so too did black music, which has grown and ramified, dramatically affecting the development of American music in general. The result is that today, more than ever before, black music provides a powerful lens through which we may view the history of black Americans in a new and revealing w v.

Scott Joplin's opera Treemonisha was the most ambitious work to emerge from the ragtime period. Sadly, however, the opera was a commercial failure when it opened in Harlem in 1915. Jelly Roll Morton was the first great figure in the new music known as jazz. Morton was influenced by Scott Joplin and often used ragtime techniques in his compositions.

This traditional folk song is a perfect example of the type of early popular music that eventually gave birth to the ragtime phenomenon. The repeated syncopation in every other measure foreshadows later ragtime compositions, and the subject matter (an implied conversation between a man who is on the run from the law and the woman he hopes will give him a place to stay) is also a taste of things to come.

BED ON THE FLOOR

Make me a bed right down on the floor, ba - by,

Make me a bed right down on the floor, And

I'll lay my head on that bed on the floor.

Chorus   Bed on the floor, baby, bed on the floor,
Bed on the floor, baby, bed on the floor,
And I'll lay my head on the bed on the floor.

Sheriff on my trail with a big forty-four,
Sheriff on my trail with a big forty-four,
And I'll lay my head on that bed on the floor.   *Chorus*

Clock striking midnight, daylight to go,
Clock striking midnight, daylight to go,
And I'll lay my head on the bed on the floor.   *Chorus*

This melody has a long and interesting history. It first appeared in the venerable old English song "The Courtship of the Frog and the Mouse," better known in this country as "Froggie Went A-Courtin'." "Crawdad," however, is a faster, more syncopated variant of the original tune. The song's bouncy, catchy phrases made it a favorite among ragtime composers, who borrowed from it freely and inserted its lyrics and melody into many of their own creations. Traces of the song will be easily recognized in two of the other compositions included in this collection, "You've Been a Good Old Wagon" and "Possumala."

CRAWDAD

You get   a line and   I'll   get a pole, ___ hon -ey, _____

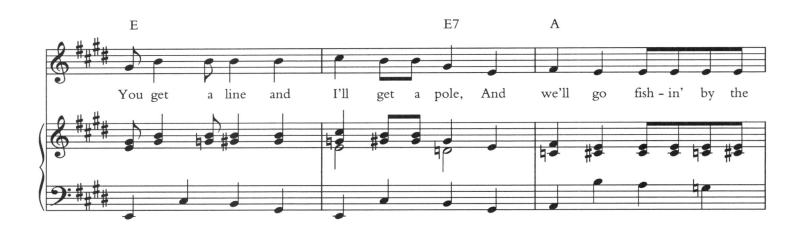

Yonder comes a man with a pack on his back . . .
Totin' all the crawdads he can pack . . .

A-settin' on the ice till my feet got cold . . .
A-watchin' that crawdad dig his hole . . .

Crawdad, crawdad, you'd better dig deep . . .
For I'm a-goin' to ramble in my sleep . . .

A-settin' on the ice till my feet got hot . . .
A-watchin' that crawdad rack and trot . . .

Crawdad, crawdad, you'd better go to hole . . .
If I don't catch you, damn my soul . . .

Whatcha gonna do when the lake runs dry? . . .
Sit on the bank and watch the crawdads die . . .

In addition to an insistent, syncopated rhythmic pattern, "Duncan and Brady" has another important element that points the way to ragtime and jazz compositions—its creative use of harmony. The song's chromatic chord progressions sound as if they might have been conceived by jazz giants Jelly Roll Morton or Fats Waller.

DUNCAN AND BRADY

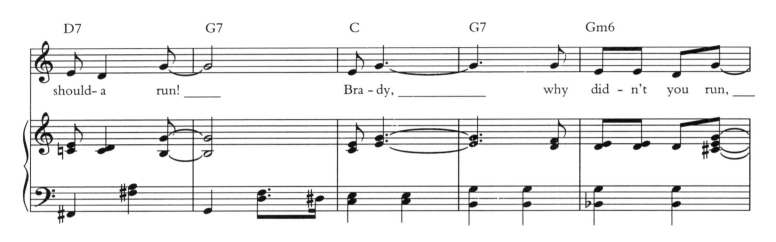

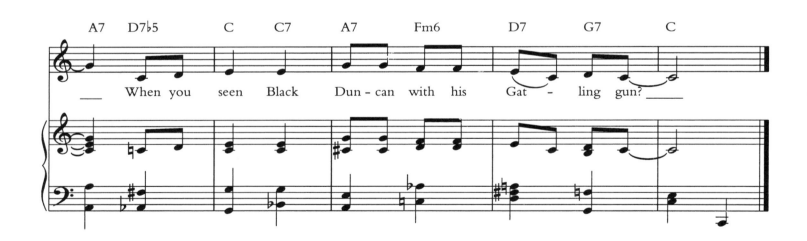

Brady, he lit out toward the door,
Duncan pulled out his big forty-four.
He shot him once and he shot him twice
Saying, "That'll take care of your cheatin' at dice." *Chorus*

Brady, he staggered and fell to the ground.
Duncan said, "You're on your last go 'round.
I told you a dozen times or more,
And now you lie dead on the barroom floor." *Chorus*

Brady went to hell lookin' mighty curious,
The devil says, "Where you from?" "East St. Louis."
"Well, pull off your coat and step this way,
For I've been expecting you every day!" *Chorus*

When the girls heard that Brady was dead
They went up home and put on red,
And came down town singin' this song:
"Brady's struttin' in hell with his Stetson on!" *Chorus*

Final Chorus:

Brady, oh, where you at?
Brady, where you at?
Brady, where you at?
Just a-struttin' in hell with his Stetson hat!

Pianist Jelly Roll Morton (born Ferdinand Joseph La Menthe) and his band, the Red Hot Peppers, were widely popular during the 1920s. Morton's song "Jelly Roll Blues," published in 1915, is probably the first jazz piece ever printed.

This is the finale of the Joplin opera. Instructions for the dance are as follows: 1. The Slow Drag must begin on the first beat of each measure. 2. When moving forward, drag the left foot: when moving backward, drag the right foot. 3. When moving sideways to the right, drag the left foot; when moving sideways to the left, drag the right foot. 4. When prancing, your steps must come on the first beat of each measure. 5. When marching and sliding, your steps must come on the first and third beats of each measure. 6. Hop and skip on second beat of measure. Double the schottische step to fit the slow music.

A Real Slow Drag

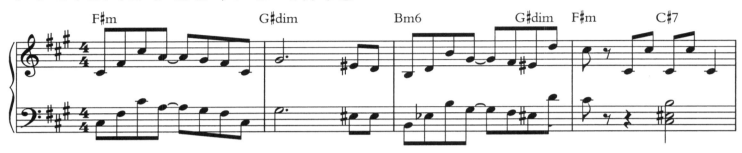

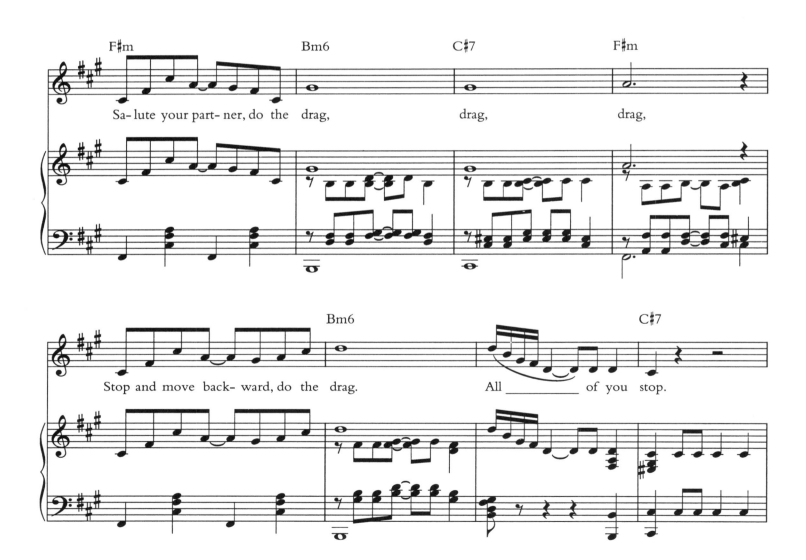

Willie got high to a syncopated melody in a minor key. In later versions of the song, Willie was renamed *"Minnie the Moocher"* and *her* misadventures were made famous by the great Harlem jazz singer Cab Calloway.

WILLIE THE WEEPER

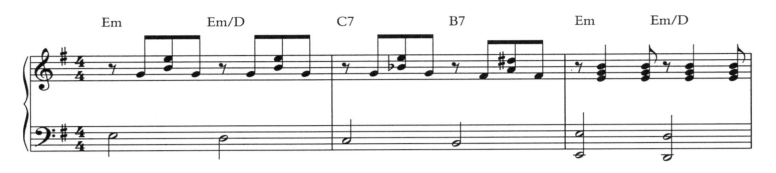

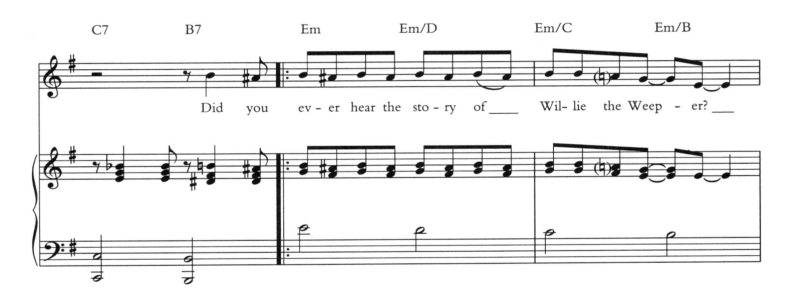

Did you ev - er hear the sto - ry of ____ Wil- lie the Weep - er? ___

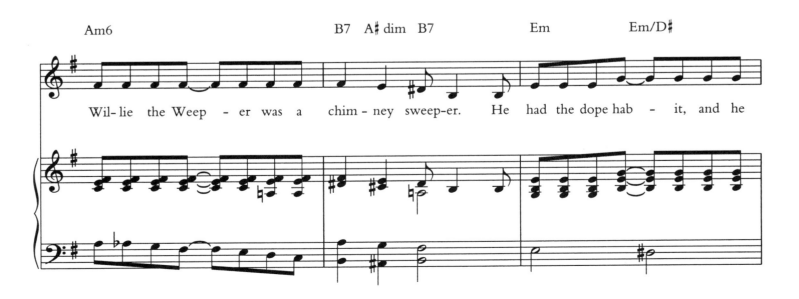

Wil- lie the Weep - er was a chim - ney sweep-er. He had the dope hab - it, and he

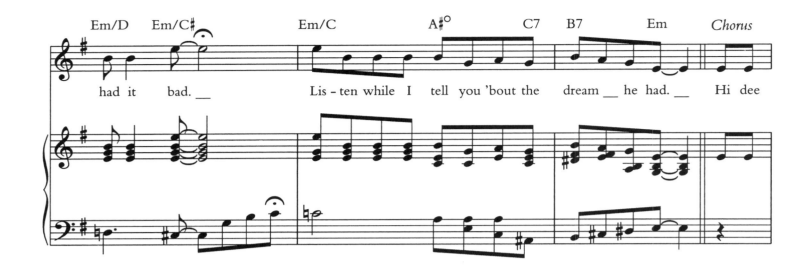

had it bad. __ Lis-ten while I tell you 'bout the dream __ he had. __ Hi dee

1.

Final Ending

hi dee hi, __ Ho di ho __ dee ho. __ ho __ dee ho. __

He went down to the dope house one Saturday night,
When he knew that all the lights would be burning bright.
He must have smoked a dozen pills or more,
When he woke up he was on a foreign shore. *Chorus*

Well, the Queen of Sheba was the first he met,
She called him her darling and her loving pet.
She gave him a great big automobile,
With a diamond headlight and a gold steering wheel. *Chorus*

He landed with a splash in the River Nile,
A-riding a domesticated crocodile.
He winked at Cleopatra — she said, "Ain't he a sight,
How about a date for next Saturday night?" *Chorus*

Down in Monte Carlo he won every bet,
Made a million dollars just a-playing roulette.
He broke the Czar of Russia — what a joke!
So Willie took another pill and rolled a smoke. *Chorus*

He had a million cattle and he had a million sheep,
He had a million vessels the ocean deep.
He had a million dollars in nickels and dimes,
He knew 'cause he had counted it a million times.　　*Chorus*

He landed in New York one evening late,
And asked his sugar for an after date.
Willie got funny, she began to shout—
When, bim bam boo! the dope gave out.　　*Chorus*

The song "Willie the Weeper" achieved its greatest fame in Harlem in the 1930s and '40s when Cotton Club singer-bandleader Cab Calloway transformed it into the tale of "Minnie the Moocher."

The poet Carl Sandburg was 22 years old in 1900. Ragtime music was in the air at the time, its syncopated rhythms heard in clubs and music halls across the nation. The ragtime song "Tell Old Bill" inspired Sandburg. After first hearing the song, the young poet wrote admiringly, "It is a monotone of life in songtones of dusk colors and rhythms that emerge from the shadows."

TELL OLD BILL

Tell old Bill __ when he comes home __ this morn-ing. _____

Tell old Bill __ when he comes home __ this eve - ning. _____

Tell old Bill __ when he comes home, To leave them down-town gals a - lone; __ This

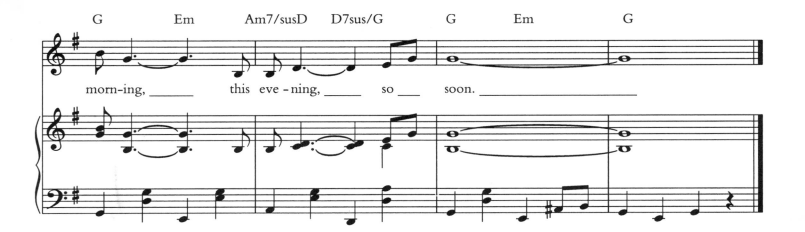

morn-ing, _____ this eve-ning, _____ so ___ soon. _____

Old Sal was baking bread this morning,
Old Sal was baking bread this evening,
Old Sal was baking bread,
When she found out her Bill was dead.
This morning, this evening, so soon.

She said, "Oh, no, it can't be so," this morning,
She said, "Oh, no, it can't be so," this evening,
She said, "Oh, no, this can't be,
They killed my Bill in the third degree."
This morning, this evening, so soon.

The brought Bill home in a hurry - up wagon this morning,
They brought Bill home in a hurry - up wagon this evening,
They brought Bill home in a hurry - up wagon,
Poor dead Bill—how his toes were draggin'.
This morning, this evening, so soon.

The cakewalk was developed from a "prize walk" done in the days of slavery, generally at large get-togethers on the plantation. It was later performed at minstrel shows with some of the male performers dressing up as women to act as walking partners for the others. The fancy, high-stepping movements of the couples along with the rollicking musical accompaniment captivated audiences everywhere.

WALKING FOR THAT CAKE

Words by Ed Hamgan
Music by Dave Braham

'Twas down at Aun - tie Jack - son's, There was a big re - cep - tion, Of high - toned so - cie - ty peo - ple, so full of sweet af - fec - tion. Such sing - ing and such danc - ing, We made the ceil - ing shake. The cream of all the eve - ning was A - walk - ing for that

use, we can't keep still. O, please to stop that mu - sic! O, do, for good - ness

sake! I feel so shy, I'll real - ly die, A - walk - ing for that cake.

Fine

Cakewalk dances were extremely popular throughout the United States during the mid-1890s. The spirited dances were often accompanied by ragtime music.

This song pays tribute to the black stevedores who worked the rivers and seaports of 19th-century America. Workers had to be rough, tough, and strong to survive that unforgiving life. The main character in this song was obviously one of the roughest, toughest, and strongest ever to work the docks. Charles E. Trevathan adapted this song in 1896 from an old roustabout song from St. Louis and dedicated his version to singer May Irwin. May and her sister Flo were instrumental in bringing ragtime singing into white music halls. In 1927 music critic Sigmund Spaeth wrote the following words about May Irwin and the "good old days" of ragtime: "May Irwin will always be remembered as the real mother of ragtime in America, and the song that did the trick was 'The Bully.'"

THE NEW BULLY SONG

Words and Music by
Charles E. Trevathan

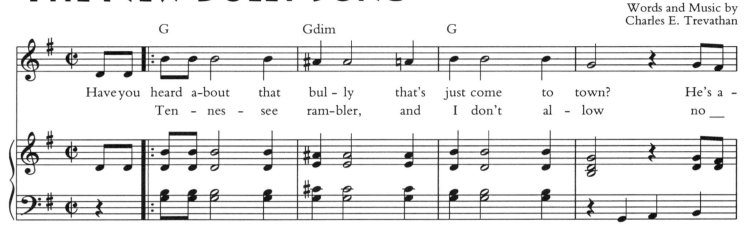

Have you heard a-bout that bul - ly that's just come to town? He's a -
Ten - nes - see ram-bler, and I don't al - low no __

round a - mong the poor folks, __ And a lay- in' their bod - ies down. I'm a -
red - eyed riv - er roust-a- bout with __ me __ to raise a row. I'm a -

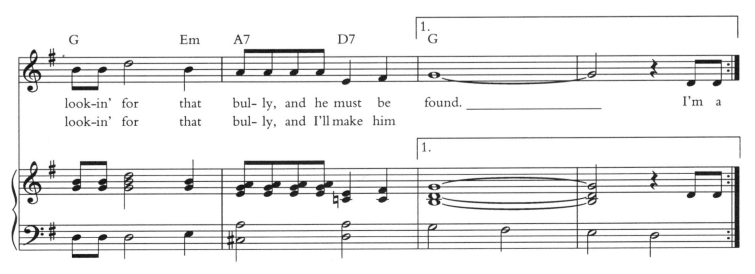

look-in' for that bul- ly, and he must be found. _____ I'm a
look-in' for that bul- ly, and I'll make him

23

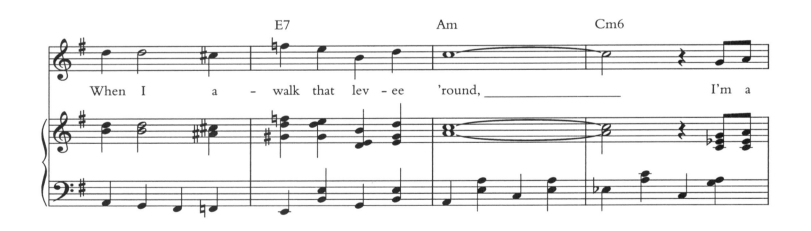

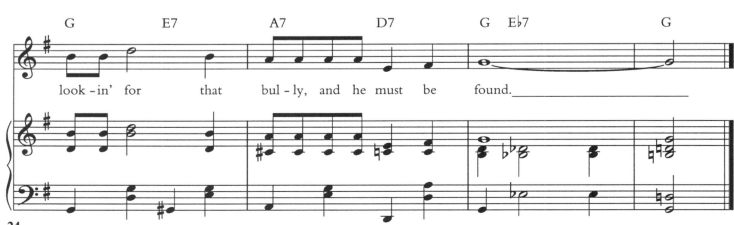

I'm going down the street with my ax in my hand,
I'm looking for that bully and I'll sweep him off this land,
I'm a-looking for that bully and he must be found.
I'll take 'long my razor, I'm going to carve him deep,
And when I see that bully, I'll lay him down to sleep,
I'm looking for that bully and he must be found.   *Chorus*

I went to a wingin' down at Parson Jones,
Took along my trusty blade to carve that fella's bones,
Just a-looking for that bully, hear his groans.
I walked in the front door, the men were prancing high,
For that levee fella I skinned my foxy eye,
Just a-looking for that bully but he wasn't nigh.   *Chorus*

I asked Miss Pansy Blossom if she would wing a reel,
She says, "Law, Mr. Johnsing, how high you make me feel."
Then you ought to see me shake my sugar heel.
I rose up like a black cloud and took a look around,
There was that new bully standing on the ground.
I've been looking for you, fella, and I've got you found.   *Chorus*

When I got through with that bully, a doctor and a nurse
Weren't no good to that man, so they put him in a hearse,
A cyclone couldn't have tore him up much worse.
You don't hear 'bout that fella that treated folks so free,
Go down upon the levee and his face you'll never see,
There's only one boss bully, and that one is me.   *Chorus*

When you see me coming, hoist your windows high,
When you see me going, hang your heads and cry,
I'm a-looking for that bully and he must die.
My madness is a-rising and I'm not going to get left,
I'm getting so bad that I'm askeered of myself,
I was looking for that bully now he's on the shelf.   *Chorus*

With an 1895 copyright date, "Wagon" is the first ragtime song ever to appear in print, and its composer, Benjamin Robertson Harney, was among the pioneers of ragtime music. An itinerant piano player from Kentucky, Harney first played his innovative music for patrons of the cheap, dingy saloons of Louisville, Kentucky. After selling the song to a New York firm for $25, Harney traveled to New York City, where he became an overnight sensation in Tony Pastor's Music Hall.

You've Been a Good Old Wagon but You Done Broke Down

Words and Music by
Harney and Biller

I was stand-ing in a crap game, do-in' no harm, ___ Ba - by!

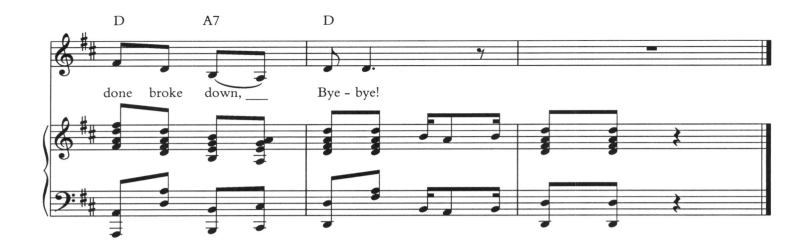

done broke down,___ Bye - bye!

As ragtime became more popular, bigger bands began to play the syncopated tunes in large music halls. The Ragtime Vaudeville Company (pictured here) was typical of the makeshift ensembles that toured the country during the early 20th century.

Benjamin R. Harney was a well-known vaudeville comedian and musician during the early days of ragtime. Never burdened by modesty, he described himself as "an absolute hit everywhere" and "the inventor of ragtime." But Harney's confidence was well founded. He quickly followed the success of "You've Been a Good Old Wagon" with another hit, "Mister Johnson, Turn Me Loose." A later critic described the song as "the first archaic beginnings of the universal, migrant Negro lament that we now call the blues. The song contains elements of both the blues and ragtime, skillfully woven together in an authentic, folksy fashion."

MISTER JOHNSON, TURN ME LOOSE

Words and Music by Ben Harney

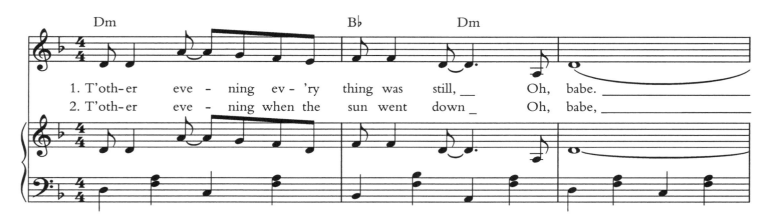

1. T'oth-er eve - ning ev - 'ry thing was still, __ Oh, babe. _____
2. T'oth-er eve - ning when the sun went down __ Oh, babe, _____

The moon was climb - ing down be - hind the hill, __ Oh,
I went down to ___ old John-son's chick - en farm, _ Oh,

babe. _____ Thought ev - 'ry bod - y was a -
babe. _____ Climbed in the chick -en loft up -

One fel-la's name was a-Lit-tle Joe __ Bet-ting six bits t'a quar-ter he could
Pic-ture me there just a - look-in' for chick-ens, When a great big bull-dog be-gan a -

make the four. __ He made that point but he made no more:
rais - in' the dick - ens, Now I climbed high - er, the chick-ens got nigh - er,

Refrain

Just then John - son jumped through the door. Oh, Mis - ter
Just then John - son o - pened fire. I got no

John - son, turn me loose, Got no mon - ey but a good ex -
chance for to be turned loose, Got no chance __ for a good ex -

Ragtime songs with "African" or "Ethiopian" settings were all the rage at the turn of the century, and composers strove to outdo one another in their choices of exotic locales. In 1902 the musical comedy team of Bob Cole and J. Rosamund Johnson penned this all-time favorite. True to the spirit of the times, the song combined a catchy tune with all the necessary ingredients for a hit: "the jungle," "a Zulu from Matabooloo," a "dusky" maiden, and, of course, "a bamboo tree."

UNDER THE BAMBOO TREE

Words by Bob Cole
Music by J. Rosamond Johnson

if you - a love - a me, One live as two,

two live as one, Un-der the bam-boo tree.

And in this simple jungle way,
He wooed the maiden ev'ry day,
By singing what he had to say.
One day he seized her and gently squeezed her,
And there beneath the bamboo green
He begged her to become his queen.
The dusky maiden blushed unseen
And joined him in his song: *Chorus*

This little story, strange but true,
Is often told in Mataboo,
Of how this Zulu tried to woo
His jungle lady in tropics shady.
Although the scene was miles away,
Right here at home, I dare to say,
You'll hear some Zulu ev'ry day
Gush out this soft refrain: *Chorus*

The songwriting team of Bob Cole and J. Rosamund Johnson wrote many hit musical comedies and a number of popular ragtime songs, including "Under the Bamboo Tree."

The poet Paul Laurence Dunbar and composer-conductor Will Marion Cook collaborated on this popular "coon song." Today the term is racially charged and understandably offensive. For turn-of-the-century black artists like Dunbar and Cook, however, the songs of this genre evoked the simple lifestyles and colorful folkways of rural African Americans. There were few opportunities for black people to tell their own story during the 1890s, even in a stereotypical fashion, and Dunbar and Cook paved the way for the more sophisticated black artist who would follow them in the 20th century.

WHO DAT SAY CHICKEN IN DIS CROWD

Words by Paul Laurence Dunbar
Music by Will Marion Cook

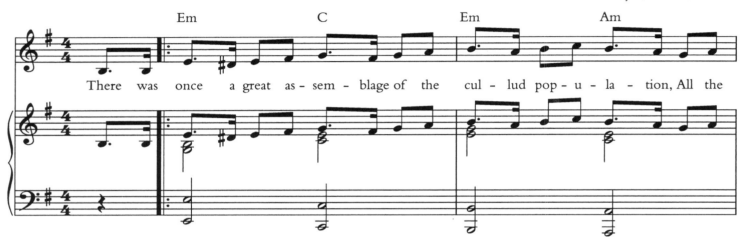

The great African-American poet Paul Laurence Dunbar was an early admirer of ragtime music. Dunbar's evocative poem "When Malindy Sings" captured the music's early spirit. "But hit's Sousa played in ragtime," he wrote in the popular dialect of the period, "an' hit's Rastus on Parade, W'en de colo'ed ban' comes ma'chin' down de street."

Composed in 1894, Irving Jones's "Possumala" was a takeoff on the Creole dance "Pas Ma La." A comedian as well as a songwriter, Jones combined his talents to make innocent, humorous, but often biting comments on the social conditions of his day.

POSSUMALA

Words and Music by Irving Jones

night I went to a col-ored hop, The house was guard-ed by fif-ty cops, And

when the men be-gan to dance, You ought to seen dem wen-ches prance. They did the

black gal there was dressed in yal-ler, Her hair was plas-tered wid mut-ton tal-ler, She
was the man who ran the ball. The dance was held at Bad Land Hall, And
he, "I must have things my way, So don't you play me for a jay, If you

was the tough-est gal in town, She could do all the oth-er gals up brown. In
Bad Land Pete was ser-geant at arms, At times you could hear him yell, "Keep calm." Says,
do I'll bust this jam - bo - ree, And there won't be a man in here but me." Says,

he, "I've guns and ra-zors to let, So get your part-ners for a set," And

sit - ting on a big high loft, This is how he called the "fig-gers" off:

All hands 'round, wheel and spin, Let me see you do the jay - bird gin, In -
thought them men would have a fit when he said, "Ev-'ry-one walk in - to it." All
cite -ment now was at its height, When in came a big guy look-in' for fight, Said
pulled his gun, be - gan to shoot, All the dan -cers they be - gan to scoot! Such
cops came in, got that bad man, And slipped the nip -pers on his hands, For

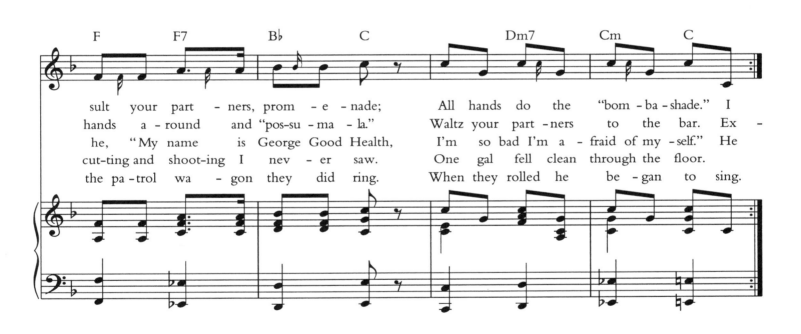

sult your part - ners, prom - e - nade; All hands do the "bom - ba - shade." I
hands a - round and "pos-su - ma - la." Waltz your part -ners to the bar. Ex -
he, "My name is George Good Health, I'm so bad I'm a - fraid of my -self." He
cut-ting and shoot-ing I nev - er saw. One gal fell clean through the floor.
the pa -trol wa - gon they did ring. When they rolled he be - gan to sing.

Chorus

No - bo-dy knows how_ bad I am,___ hon - ey! hon - ey!

No - bo-dy knows how bad I am, baby! baby!

No - bo-dy knows how bad I am, If you fool with me, You'll get

in a jam, My dar-ling, my loved one, my H - O - N - E -

Y!

James P. Johnson was an early representative of the New York school of stride piano and the first great jazz pianist. Johnson's virtuoso technique influenced pianists as diverse as Fats Waller, Art Tatum, Thelonious Monk, and Cecil Taylor.

The publication of "The Maple Leaf Rag Song" in 1899 changed the course of American popular music. The song quickly became a national hit, its popularity exceeding the wildest dreams of its publisher, John Stark, and its composer, 30-year-old Scott Joplin. The song's success fueled an explosion of ragtime music by both black and white composers across the country. The song would become Joplin's trademark over the years, as he played it at ragtime piano contests and orchestrated it for marching band. The lyrics were later added by Sidney Brown and only served to heighten the song's popularity.

THE MAPLE LEAF RAG SONG

Words by Sidney Brown
Music by Scott Joplin

1. I come from old Vir-gin-ny, From the coun-ty Ac-o-mac. I -
2. I dropped in-to the swell-est ball, The great ex-clu-sive It. But my
3. The men were struck with jeal-ous-y, The pis-tols 'gan to flash. But the

have no wealth to speak of, 'rept the clothes up-on my back. I can
face was dead a-gin me, And my trous-ers did-n't fit. But when
la-dies gath-ered 'round me, For I'd sure-ly made a mash. The

do the coun-try hoe-down, I can buck and wing to show, down, And
Ma-ple Leaf was start-ed, My tim-i-di-ty de-part-ed, I
fin-est belle, she sent a boy to call a coach and pair, We

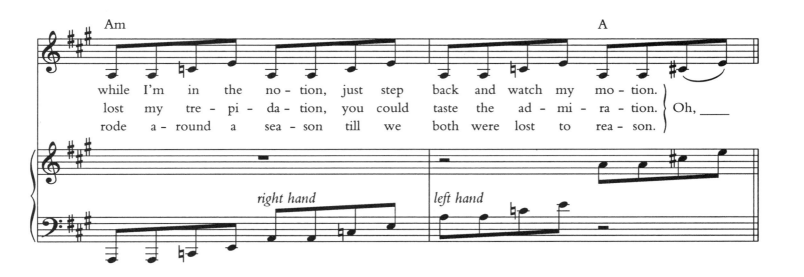

while I'm in the no - tion, just step back and watch my mo - tion.
lost my tre - pi - da - tion, you could taste the ad - mi - ra - tion. } Oh, ____
rode a - round a sea - son till we both were lost to rea - son.

right hand

left hand

Refrain

go 'way man, I can hyp - no - tize this na - tion, I can
go 'way man, just hold your breath a min - ute, For there's

shake the earth's foun - da - tion with the Ma - ple Leaf Rag. Oh, ____ Ma - ple Leaf Rag.
not a stunt that's in it with the

Joplin conceived of the *The Ragtime Dance* as a sort of folk ballet, with narrative soloist and choreography based on popular dances of the day. His ambition was to break the restrictive mold of simple ragtime and develop larger, more ambitious compositions. Joplin's publisher, John Stark, refused to print the entire work. It was, after all, nine printed pages long and took more than twenty minutes to perform. The typical ragtime piece of the day consisted of four sixteen-measure sections and was seldom longer than four pages. The entire work was first performed at Wood's Opera House in Sedalia, Missouri, in 1899. Joplin himself funded the production. This song is an excerpt from the score.

THE RAGTIME DANCE SONG

Words and Music by Scott Joplin

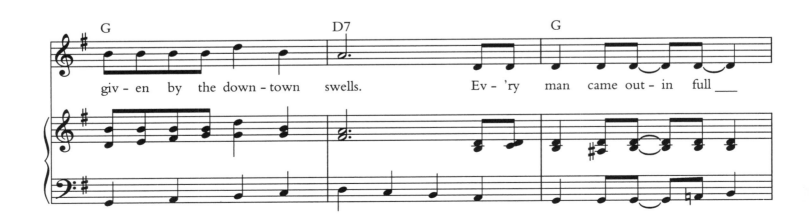

most pop-u-lar mel-o dies of the day. All the cou-ples took their plac-es, All the

men had smil-ing fac-es, While they wait-ed for the call-er to say: Well, ___

Refrain **a tempo**

Let me see you do the Rag-time Dance, Turn ___ left and do the cake-walk prance.
Let me see you do the "Clean-up Dance," Now you do the "Jen-nie Cool-er Dance."

Turn the oth-er way and do the slow drag. Now you take your la-dy to the

Pianist Lucky Roberts was one of the early masters of the stride piano technique invented by Scott Joplin. Roberts's compositions "Junk Man Rag" and "Pork and Beans" were among the most popular tunes of the ragtime period.

Despite the disappointing reception of *The Ragtime Dance*, Joplin never gave up the idea of composing a larger work. His main ambition was to compose a ragtime opera. Joplin completed *Treemonisha* in 1907, but it would take another eight years before he was able to mount a live production of it in Harlem—and that at his own expense! Sadly, the opera was a commercial failure. Black audiences had little patience for the composer's operatic ambitions, and it would be many years before the white establishment was prepared to acknowledge Joplin's achievement. "We're Goin' Around," a lively, cornhusking ring dance, is the opera's opening number.

WE'RE GOIN' AROUND

1. Dere was a man be - fo' de war, O, we're go-in' a-round. Said
2. All join hands an' cir-cle once mo', O, we're go-in' a-round. __

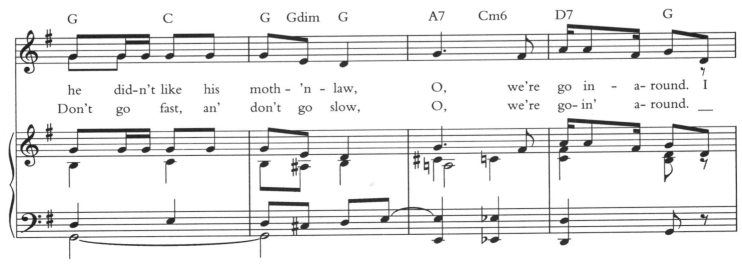

he did-n't like his moth-'n-law, O, we're go in - a-round. I
Don't go fast, an' don't go slow, O, we're go-in' a-round. __

This is another exuberant dance number from Joplin's opera. It is performed by the main character, Treemonisha, and a group of field-workers at "quittin' time."

Aunt Dinah Has Blowed de Horn

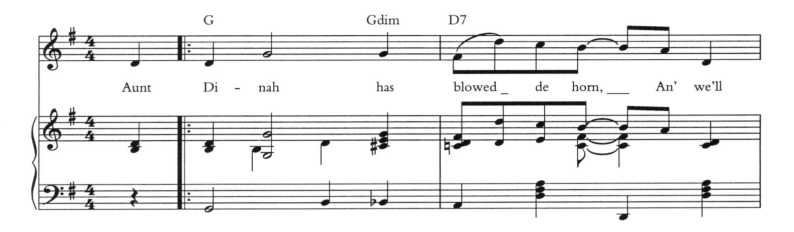

Aunt Di - nah has blowed _ de horn, ___ An' we'll

go home to stay un - til dawn. ____ Get read - y, put yo'

sack on yo' back, _ I'm so hap- py I don't know how to act, Aunt

Di-nah has blowed de horn,__ An' she wants us to come__ straight home,____ we have not much time for de-lay,__ 'Cause our work is fin-ished for to-day. O yes, Aunt day.

According to ragtime legend, song and dance man Hughie Cannon once gave the price of a hotel room to Bill Bailey of the vaudeville team Bailey and Cowan. Bailey had apparently been locked out of his own home by his exasperated wife. The incident stuck in Cannon's mind, and in 1902 he wrote this festive song about a lonely wife's plea to her wayward but lovable husband. Over the years, "Bill Bailey" has been performed and recorded by hundreds of entertainers. It has become an anthem for both ragtime music and Dixieland jazz.

BILL BAILEY, WON'T YOU PLEASE COME HOME?

Words and Music by Hughie Cannon

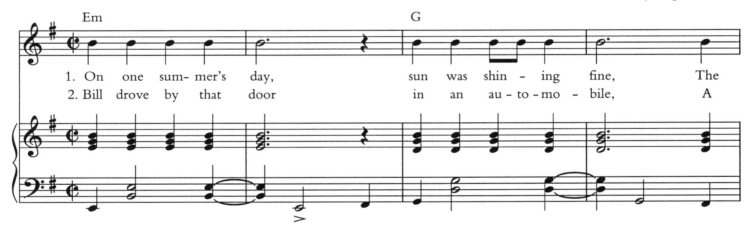

1. On one sum-mer's day, sun was shin-ing fine, The
2. Bill drove by that door in an au-to-mo-bile, A

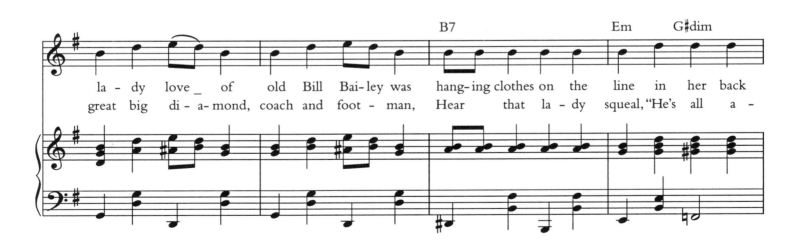

la-dy love _ of old Bill Bai-ley was hang-ing clothes on the line in her back
great big di-a-mond, coach and foot-man, Hear that la-dy squeal, "He's all a-

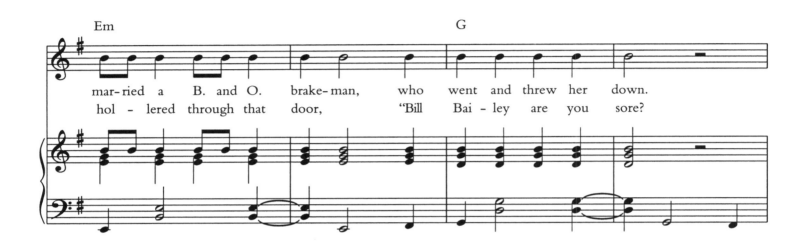

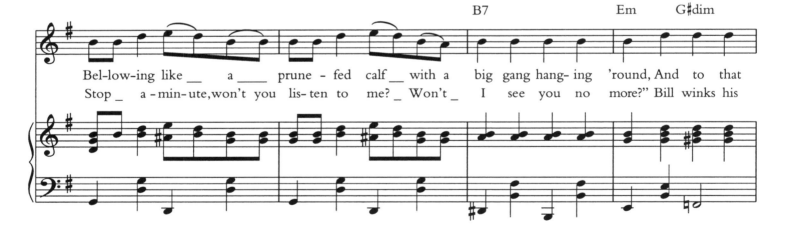

Won't you come home, Bill Bai - ley, won't you come home?

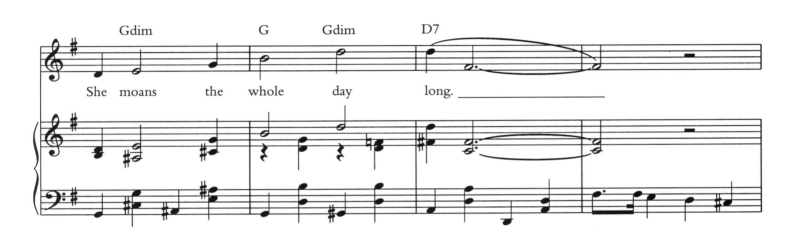

She moans the whole day long. _____

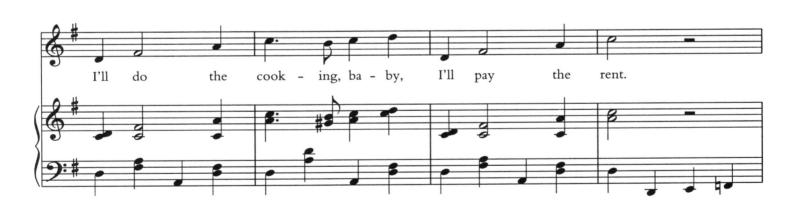

I'll do the cook - ing, ba - by, I'll pay the rent.

I know I done you wrong _____

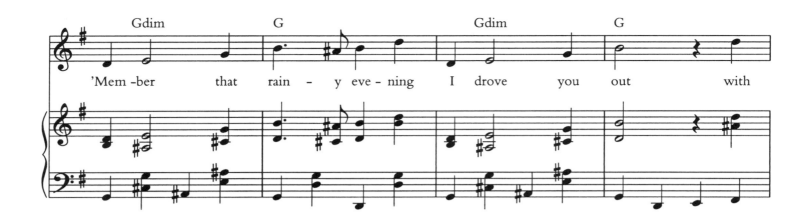

'Mem-ber that rain - y eve-ning I drove you out with

noth - ing but a fine - tooth comb? _____ I

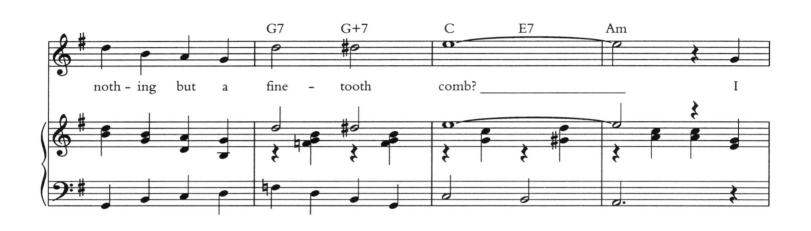

know I'm to blame, Well ___ ain't it a shame? Bill

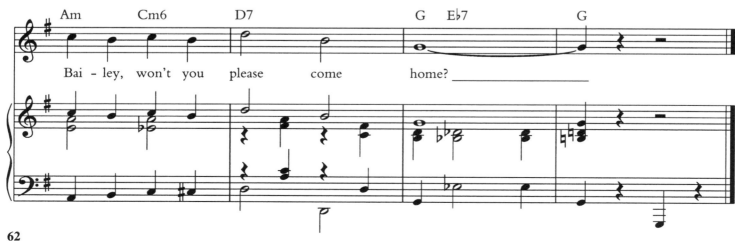

Bai - ley, won't you please come home? _____

Not only was Bill Bailey the main character in this popular tune, he was also one-half of the popular vaudeville team Bailey and Cowan.

Jerry Silverman is one of America's most prolific authors of music books. He has a B.S. degree in music from the City College of New York and an M.A. in musicology from New York University. He has authored some 100 books dealing with various aspects of guitar, banjo, violin, and fiddle technique, as well as numerous songbooks and arrangements for other instruments. He teaches guitar and music to children and adults and performs in folk-song concerts before audiences of all ages.

Kenneth B. Clark received a Ph.D. in social psychology from Columbia University and is the author of numerous books and articles on race and education. His books include *Prejudice and Your Child*, *Dark Ghetto*, and *Pathos of Power*. Long noted as an authority on segregation in schools, his work was cited by the U.S. Supreme Court in its decision in the historic *Brown v. Board of Education of Topeka* case in 1954. Dr. Clark, Distinguished Professor of Psychology Emeritus at the City University of New York, is the president of Kenneth B. Clark & Associates, a consulting firm specializing in personnel matters, race relations, and affirmative action programs.